FURTHER FOURTH YEAR ASSESSMENT PAPERS IN
MATHEMATICS

PUPIL'S BOOK

J M BOND

Nelson

Paper 1

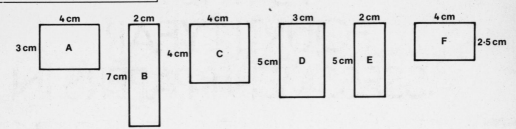

1. Area of A is
   .... cm²

2. Area of B is
   .... cm²

3. Area of C is
   .... cm²

4. Perimeter of A is
   .... cm

5. Perimeter of B is
   .... cm

6. Perimeter of C is
   .... cm

7. Area of D is
   .... cm²

8. Area of E is
   .... cm²

9. Area of F is
   .... cm²

10. Perimeter of D is
    .... cm

11. Perimeter of E is
    .... cm

12. Perimeter of F is
    .... cm

13. If the shapes were covered with small squares
    1 cm × 1 cm, which two shapes would need the
    same number of squares?   ....

14–15. If a piece of cord were put round the outside
    of each shape, which shapes would need the
    same length of cord?   ....

Write the number which is:

16. 2 less than 700 ....

17. 10 more than one thousand ....

18. 20 less than 2000 ....

19. 30 more than 2890 ....

20–24. Class 4A has 24 children. One day 6 were absent.
    What was the ratio of those who were present to those
    who were absent?   ....

    What fraction of the class was present?   ....

2

What fraction was absent? ....

What percentage of the class was away? ....

What percentage of the class was present? ....

25	2938 +3746	26	241 −147	27	357 ×6	28	7)1253

Look at the following times carefully, then write either am or pm in each space.

29	10.30	School playtime
30	1.45	Afternoon school starts
31	4.15	We get home from school
32	7.30	We get up
33	8.30	We go to bed
34	7.00	We have our supper
35	8.05	We have our breakfast
36	12.30	School dinner

37–40 Complete the figures below. The dotted line is the line of symmetry.

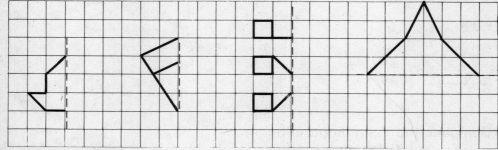

Fill each space with the sign > or < to indicate which is the larger.

41 1·7 kg   1657 g

42 1·8 l   1801 ml

43 days in July   days in June

44 $(3\frac{1}{2} + 2\frac{1}{4})$ $(7\frac{1}{2} - 2\frac{1}{4})$

45 days in 1989   days in 1988

46 (8 × 7)   (5 × 11)

47 20 hours   1 day

48 4·9 cm   56 mm

49	£27·85 +36·97	50	£41·10 −27·19

Paper 2

1–6 Write the number of degrees contained in each of the following angles.

one right angle

....

two right angles

....

half a right angle

....

⅙ of a circle

....

three right angles

....

1½ right angles

....

7 £36·27
　　　× 5
　———————

8　　　£
　　9)179·28

9–16 Complete the Venn diagram below.
Set A = multiples of 3 < 18.
Set B = multiples of 4 < 18.
Set C = multiples of 8 < 18.

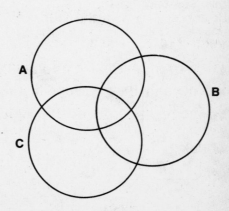

Insert brackets to make each sum correct.

17   $17 \times 2 + 4 = 102$ 18 $8 + 7 \times 2 = 30$

19   $100 + 15 \times 2 = 130$ 20 $3 + 4 \times 2 = 11$

21   $6 - 5 \times 3 = 3$ 22 $2 \times 8 + 3 = 22$

23   $10 + 10 \times 4 = 50$ 24 $60 - 10 \times 2 = 100$

25   $\frac{1}{2} + \frac{7}{8} =$ ....   26 $1 - \frac{7}{10} =$ ....

27   $\frac{3}{4} \times \frac{6}{9} =$ ....   28 $\frac{6}{9} \div \frac{2}{3} =$ ....

Round off the numbers below to the nearest 10.

29   78   30   91   31   105   32   63 ....

33   243   34   367   35   474   36   1012 ....

37   $7{\cdot}8 + 12{\cdot}95 + 0{\cdot}176 =$ ....

38   From $20{\cdot}2$ take $17{\cdot}07$ ....

39   Multiply $35{\cdot}6$ by $1{\cdot}1$ ....

40   Divide $72{\cdot}8$ by $0{\cdot}4$ ....

A number is squared when it is multiplied by itself. For example: $10^2 = 10 \times 10$. From this we see that 10 is the square root of 100. What is the square root of

41   49   42   121   43   81   44   144 ....

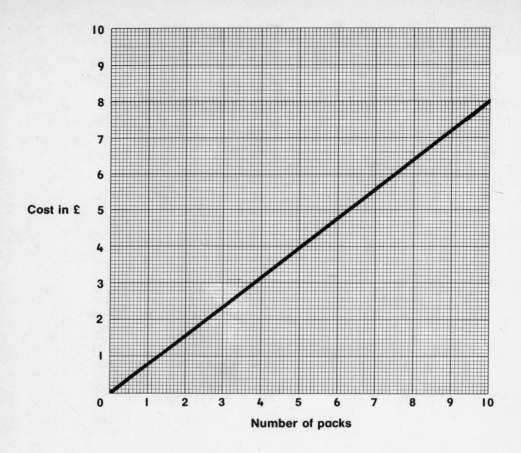

Cost in £

Number of packs

Small tablets of soap are sold in packs costing 80p each. From the graph find:

45   How many packs I can buy for £7·20.   ....

46   How much 15 packs would cost.   ....

47   How much 20 packs would cost.   ....

48   How many packs I could buy for £24·00. ....

49   How many packs I could buy for £20·00. ....

50   How much 12 packs would cost.   ....

6

Paper 3

Here is a graph which shows the percentage of boys and girls who passed a certain test during a 5-year period. Boys are marked ■ and girls ☐

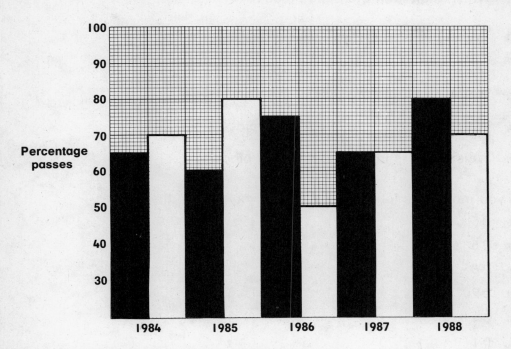

1 The average pass mark for the boys was ....

2 The average pass mark for the girls was ....

3 In which year did the boys gain the highest marks? ....

4 In which year did the girls gain their highest marks? ....

5 Which was the worst year for the boys? ....

6 Which was the worst year for the girls? ....

7 In 1985, 140 girls took the test. How many passed? ....

8 If, in 1987, 120 boys took the test, how many passed? ....

9 In which year was there no difference in the standard of the boys and girls? ....

Look carefully at the two numbers below, then answer the questions.

$$135 \cdot 79$$

10   Which digit is in the hundreds place? ....

11   Which digit is in the units place? ....

12   Which digit is in the tenths place? ....

$$46 \cdot 253$$

13   Which digit is in the tens place? ....

14   Which digit is in the hundredths place? ....

15   Which digit is in the thousandths place? ....

Can you match the following? Write the number in the space.

16	0·5 ( )	( )	$\frac{1}{4}$
17	0·6 ( )	( )	$\frac{1}{10}$
18	0·8 ( )	( )	$\frac{3}{4}$
19	0·25 ( )	( )	$\frac{3}{5}$
20	0·4 ( )	( )	$\frac{2}{5}$
21	0·1 ( )	( )	$\frac{1}{2}$
22	0·75 ( )	( )	$\frac{4}{5}$

23–29   Here is a rectangular pie-chart which shows what Jackie did with the £24·00 she was given for Christmas.

She saved .... The scarf cost ....

The game cost .... The chocolates cost ....

The book cost .... The magazines cost ....

Jackie spent .... at the disco.

Here is a pictogram which shows how many people went to the Cosy Cafe last week.

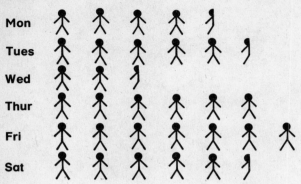

Mon	👤👤👤👤👤

= 50 people

30–35 The number of people who visited the
cafe on:

Monday was ....   Thursday was ....

Tuesday was ....   Friday was ....

Wednesday was ....   Saturday was ....

36 How many more people went to the cafe
on Thursday than on Wednesday? ....

37 On which two days did the same number
of people go to the cafe?

....

38 How many people went to the cafe that week? ....

39 If they spent an average of £3·00 each, how much money was taken
altogether? ....

40 Which day do you think was early closing day? ....

Underline the correct answer.

41 $\frac{1}{2} - \frac{1}{8} =$ $\frac{1}{6}$ $\frac{1}{10}$ $\frac{3}{8}$ $\frac{1}{2}$ $\frac{1}{4}$

42 $\frac{3}{4} \times \frac{1}{4} =$ 1 $\frac{1}{4}$ $\frac{4}{8}$ $\frac{4}{16}$ $\frac{3}{16}$

43   10% of 50 =   5   45   10   40   15

44   The number of hours in 3 days =
     60   36   84   72   90

45   The number of seconds in 5 minutes =
     60   300   360   120   200

46    $\frac{1}{2} \div 4 =$ 2 $\frac{1}{2}$ $\frac{1}{8}$ $\frac{3}{8}$ $\frac{5}{3}$

47    $24\overline{)984}$ 48 $25\overline{)700}$ 49 $\begin{array}{r} 364 \\ \times\ 25 \\ \hline \end{array}$ 50 $\begin{array}{r} 173 \\ \times\ 36 \\ \hline \end{array}$

Paper 4

1–12   Alison waited for the sales before buying new clothes. She went to the Supersaver Store where the prices were cut by 20%. Complete this table.

	Usual price	Sale price	Saving
Pleated skirt	£15·00	....	....
Sweater	£10·00	....	....
Shoes	....	£16·00	....
Jacket	....	....	£5·00
Jeans	£9·00	....	....

Altogether Alison spent .... on her new clothes.

She saved .... by waiting for the sales.

13   Share 48 items in the ratio of 3:5.   ....

14   Share 27 items in the ratio of 7:2.   ....

15   Share 36 items in the ratio of 5:4.   ....

16 Share 66 items in the ratio of 8:3. ....

17 Share 108 items in the ratio of 9:3. ....

Multiply each number below by 100.

18 47·6	**19** 12	**20** 7·2	**21** 355·8	**22** 0·014
....	....	....	....	....

23–26 In each of the classes below there are 30 children. The table shows attendances for one week this term. Find the average attendance for each class.

	Class 1A	Class 1B	Class 2A	Class 2B
Monday	27	28	30	30
Tuesday	28	23	29	25
Wednesday	30	24	28	28
Thursday	25	25	28	26
Friday	25	25	30	21
Average attendance	....	....	....	....

27 On which day were there most children at school? ....

28 On which day were the fewest children present? ....

29 Which class had full attendance on two days? ....

30 Which class had the lowest attendance on any one day? ....

31–33 At a concert there were 451 people. The boys and girls together totalled 322. The adults and boys together totalled 292. How many:

boys were there .... girls were there ....

adults were there ....

Write the following numbers in figures.

34 Twenty-three thousand and seventeen ....

35 Four hundred and two thousand and forty-two ....

36 Five hundred and fifteen thousand, five hundred and five ....

37 Ninety thousand, seven hundred and nine ....

38 One hundred and one thousand and seven ....

39 Fifty seven thousand, five hundred and seventy ....

Find the cost of: £

40 4 kg of carrots @ 37p per kg ....

41 2½ kg of sprouts @ 52p per kg ....

42 1¼ kg of onions @ 36p per kg ....

_____

43 Total ....

44 Change from a £5 note: ....

45–50 Complete the following table

Distance (km)	Time taken	Average speed (km/h)
100	4 hours	....
36	30 minutes	....
....	2½ hours	12
280	....	70
210	....	840
434	3½ hours	....

Paper 5

I How many ¼s are there in 3¾? ....

2 How many $\frac{1}{3}$s are there in $4\frac{2}{3}$? ....

3 How many $\frac{1}{5}$s are there in $3\frac{3}{5}$? ....

4 How many $\frac{1}{10}$s are there in $7\frac{7}{10}$? ....

5 How many $\frac{1}{2}$s are there in $17\frac{1}{2}$? ....

6-13 Look at the shape below. Write the co-ordinates of each corner, starting at A and going in a clockwise direction.

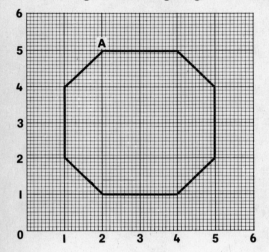

1st set .... 2nd set ....

3rd set .... 4th set ....

5th set .... 6th set ....

7th set .... 8th set ....

14 What is the name of this shape?

....

15
```
   km      m
    8      97
+   7      79
_____
```

16
```
   cm   mm
   1 1    3
 -  4     5
_____
```

17
```
   m    cm
   7    27
×         6
_____
```

18
```
   cm   mm
 5)2 7    5
```

19 The product of two numbers is 432. One number is 12, what is the other? ....

20 The sum of two numbers is 210. The larger is 179 so the smaller is ....

13

21–26 Here is the timetable of class 4a. Each lesson is 40 minutes long and the break lasts 20 minutes. Complete the timetable.

	Begins	Ends
First lesson	9.10	....
Second lesson	....	....
Break	....	10.50
Third lesson	10.50	....
Fourth lesson	....	12.10

A group of children were asked what they did last Saturday morning. Some helped with the shopping, some went for a swim, others went to the club, and 8 went to the library.

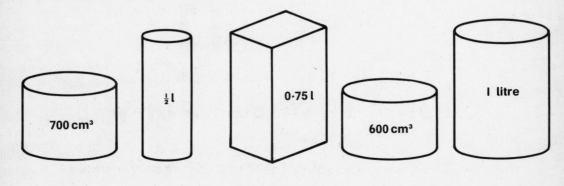

27 How many children were asked? ....

28 How many children went shopping? ....

29 How many went to the baths? ....

30 How many went to the club? ....

31 What fraction of the children went to the library? ....

32–36 Put these containers in order of capacity by writing 1 in the space under the largest and so on.

700 cm³   ½ l   0·75 l   600 cm³   1 litre

....

14

37–41 A teacher was upset to find that the price of all the music she wanted had been increased by 10%. Complete the table to show what she paid.

	Old price	New price
Carols for Juniors	£2·50	....
Recorder tunes	£1·60	....
Orchestral pieces	£2·80	....
Book of piano duets	£3·30	....
New orchestral pieces	£3·50	....

42
```
wks  days
 3    6
 5    5
+1    4
_____

_____
```

43
```
days  hrs
 7    6
-1    17
_____

_____
```

44
```
hrs  min
 5    10
×      8
_____

_____
```

45
```
min  sec
6) 73   6
```

Our group, the 'Thrushes', made this flag.

46 What is the area of the whole flag? ....

47 What is the area of the 'T'? ....

48 What is the area of the background? ....

49 The perimeter of the flag is ....

50 The perimeter of the 'T' is ....

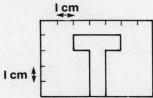

Paper 6

1–5 How many driving miles would you save if, instead of taking a ferry to St. Malo, you sailed to Santander and then drove to your destination in Spain or Portugal?

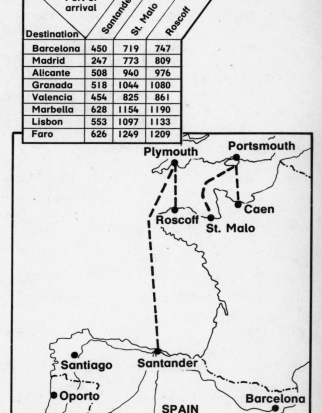

Port of arrival / Destination	Santander	St. Malo	Roscoff
Barcelona	450	719	747
Madrid	247	773	809
Alicante	508	940	976
Granada	518	1044	1080
Valencia	454	825	861
Marbella	628	1154	1190
Lisbon	553	1097	1133
Faro	626	1249	1209

You would save

To: (miles)

Lisbon   ....

Madrid   ....

Granada   ....

Faro   ....

Marbella   ....

6–10 If you took the ferry to Roscoff instead of Santander, how much further would it be to drive to:

Barcelona   ....

Alicante   ....

Valencia   ....

Madrid   ....

Lisbon   ....

11	12	13	14
4765 8439 +3856	10000 − 719	478 × 304	78)1794

15–22 We are having a party and decide to make an apple tart. The recipe we have is sufficient for 8 people. What quantities would we need for 40 people?

Apple tart (serves 8)	For 40 people
175 g plain flour	.... plain flour
100 g butter or margarine	.... butter/margarine
10 ml caster sugar	.... caster sugar
40 g ground almonds	.... ground almonds
1 egg yolk	.... egg yolks
15 ml water	.... water
25 g butter	.... butter
900 g apples	.... apples

Multiply by 10 each of the numbers below.

23 1·06   **24** 21·004   **25** 3·5   **26** 0·708   **27** 0·035

....

28 It is Sunday 28th October and the clocks have been put back during the night as Summer Time has finished. Marianne has not altered her watch, which shows 8.30. What is the correct time? ..7.30....

29–32 Put these fractions in order of size with the largest first.

$\frac{7}{12}$ $\frac{2}{3}$ $\frac{5}{6}$ $\frac{3}{4}$

....

33 How many times can I fill a glass which holds 250 ml from a jug which holds 7·5 l? ....

34 What is the difference between 27 m and 413 cm? Give your answer in cm. ....

17

35–39 Complete this spike graph which shows the heights of some children.

Number of children	Height (cm)
3	165
7	166
8	167
11	168
12	169
9	170

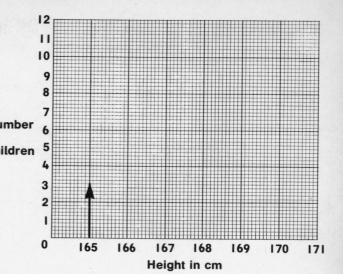

Write these times as you would see them on a digital watch.

40 7.05am   **41** 10.10pm   **42** 12.30am   **43** 10.01am   **44** 11.04pm

....

Give your answers to the following sums as mixed numbers:

45 $\frac{1}{2} + \frac{5}{8}$ **46** $\frac{3}{4} + \frac{7}{16}$ **47** $\frac{7}{8} + \frac{23}{24}$ **48** $\frac{4}{5} + \frac{3}{10}$

....

49 Add together 78p, £7·99 and £3·75.   ....

50 From 4 litres take 243 cm³. Give your answer in cm³.   ....

Paper 7

Here are the average temperatures during the coldest months of the year at some well-known holiday locations.

	Algarve	Costa Blanca	Tunisia	Israel
October	73	77	77	92
November	66	66	68	82
December	61	63	61	70
January	59	61	57	70
February	61	63	61	73
March	62	66	64	79
April	69	70	70	87

1 Which month is the coldest in all four places? ....

2 How much hotter is it in Israel than in the Algarve in October? ....

3 Which place has the greatest difference in temperature in two consecutive months? ....

4 What is the difference in temperature in these two months? ....

5 Which place has the highest temperature in any one month? ....

6 Which place has the lowest temperature in any one month? ....

7 In April, how much higher is the temperature in Israel than in the Algarve? ....

Fill in the missing number in each sum.

8 $13 \cdot 5 \times$ .... $= 135$ 9 $7 \cdot 6 \div$ .... $= 0 \cdot 076$

10 $14 \cdot 5 \div$ .... $= 0 \cdot 145$ 11 $82 \cdot 3 \times$ .... $= 823$

12 $300 \div$ .... $= 30$ 13 $0 \cdot 011 \times$ .... $= 0 \cdot 11$

14 $0 \cdot 5678 \div$ .... $= 0 \cdot 005678$ 15 $40 \cdot 4 \times$ .... $= 4040$

16–24 Match the percentages with the fractions. Write the number in the space.

10%	( )		( )	$\frac{1}{20}$
25%	( )		( )	$\frac{3}{5}$
50%	( )		( )	$\frac{3}{4}$
75%	( )		( )	$\frac{4}{5}$
5%	( )		( )	$\frac{1}{10}$
20%	( )		( )	$\frac{1}{2}$
40%	( )		( )	$\frac{2}{5}$
60%	( )		( )	$\frac{1}{4}$
80%	( )		( )	$\frac{1}{5}$

25-27 Underline any of the fractions below which are less than $\frac{1}{2}$.

$\frac{3}{7}$ $\frac{7}{10}$ $\frac{3}{4}$ $\frac{4}{9}$ $\frac{5}{6}$ $\frac{5}{11}$

Letter Post

Weight not over	1st class	2nd class	Weight not over	1st class	2nd class
60g	18p	13p	500g	92p	70p
100g	26p	20p	600g	£1·15	85p
150g	32p	24p	700g	£1·35	£1·00
200g	40p	30p	750g	£1·45	£1·05
250g	48p	37p	800g	£1·55	
300g	56p	43p	900g	£1·70	
350g	64p	49p	1000g	£1·85	
400g	72p	55p			
450g	82p	62p			

28 How much does it cost to send a first class letter weighing 180 g? ....

29 How much does it cost to send a second class letter weighing 360 g? ....

30 How much does it cost to send a first class letter weighing 702 g? ....

31 How much does it cost to send a second class letter weighing 209 g? ....

32 How much more does it cost to send a 352 g letter first class than second? ....

33 How much cheaper is it to send a 600 g letter by second rather than first class? ....

34 How much more does it cost to send a 250 g letter by first rather than second class? ....

If you turn in a clockwise direction, which way would you be facing if:

35 You are facing north and you turn through 45° ....

36 You are facing south and you turn through 180° ....

37 You are facing west and you turn through 90° ....

38 You are facing north and you turn through 135° ....

39 You are facing east and you turn through 270° ....

40 You are facing north-east and you turn through 180° ....

41 How many days are there in 47 weeks? ....

42 Turn 432 seconds into minutes and seconds. ....

43-46 What fraction of each of the shapes below is shaded?

 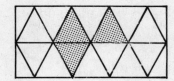

....

47 790 + 11 = ...   **48** 8989 + 21 = ...

49 998 + 23 = ...   **50** 6989 + 103 = ...

Paper 8

1 How many boats are there between 6 and 7 am Monday to Friday? ....

2 How many boats are there between 7 and 8 am Monday to Friday? ....

3 How many boats are there between 7 and 8 am on Sunday? ....

	MERSEY FERRIES TO LIVERPOOL FROM WOODSIDE		
	Mon-Fri	Sat	Sun
HRS	MINS PAST THE HOUR		
6	40	45	45
7	15 35 55	20 50	20 50
8	15 35 55	20 50	20 50
9	15 35 55	15 35 55	20 50
10	15 35 55	15 35 55	20 50
11	15 35 55	15 35 55	20 50
12	15 35 55	15 35 55	20 50
1	15 35 55	15 35 55	20 50
2	15 35 55	15 35 55	20 50
3	15 35 55	15 35 55	20 50
4	15 35 55	15 35 55	20 50
5	15 35 55	15 35 55	20 50
6	15 35 55	15 35 55	20 50
7	20 50	20 50	20 50
8	20 50	20 50	20 50
9	20	20	20

4 How many boats are there between 9 and 10 pm on Saturday? ....

5 The boats sail every .... minutes between 7 am and 7 pm Monday to Friday.

6 Between 7 am and 7 pm on Sundays the boats sail every .... minutes.

7 Write the time of the last boat each day in 24-hour-clock time. ....

8 How many more boats are there on a Wednesday than on a Sunday? ....

9
```
   yr mth
    7  8
    5  9
 +  3 10
 _____
```

10
```
   yr mth
   1 2  1
 −   5  8
 _____
```

11
```
   yr mth
    4  6
 ×     7
 _____
```

12
```
      yr mth
  5 ) 8  4
```

13–16 At Heathrow all planes do not arrive on time; some are late and some are early.

Time due	12.43		19.00
Arrived	13.04		18.54

.... minutes late early   .... minutes late early

Time due	18.51		10.10
Arrived	19.27		09.49

.... minutes late early   .... minutes late early

This pie chart shows which TV programmes are preferred by 72 children at a school. You are given the size of the angle.

17 How many children like pop music best? ....

18 The number who like sport best is ....

19 How many children like quiz programmes best? ....

20 The number who like horror films best is ....

21 How many children like plays best? ....

22 How many children like magic best? ....

23 The number who like comedies best is ....

The figures below are all regular. You are given the perimeter of each one. Work out the length of each side.

24–27

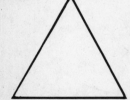 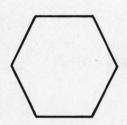 

Perimeter   13·5 cm   11·0 cm   9·3 cm   14·0 cm
Length of
one side   ....

Write *approximate* answers to the following sums:

28 39 × 20 = ...   29 39 + 69 = ...

30 300 ÷ 49 = ...   31 700 − 199 = ...

32 63 × 101 = ...   33 6000 ÷ 99 = ...

34 48 × 52 = ...   35 179 + 19 = ...

36–42 $2 = \overline{\quad5\quad} \quad \overline{\quad11\quad} \quad \overline{\quad8\quad} \quad \overline{\quad7\quad} \quad \overline{\quad12\quad} \quad \overline{\quad27\quad} \quad \overline{\quad18\quad}$

Underline the correct number of:

43	degrees in the angles all round a point	300	90	180	360	540
44	hours in a week	140	168	24	60	186
45	metres in a kilometre	1000	100	10 000	200	10
46	millimetres in 10 centimetres	10	1000	50	5	100
47	days in a leap year	365	360	165	366	200
48	pence in £100	1000	10 000	100 000	100	1100
49	minutes in $\frac{3}{4}$ hour	30	60	45	15	40
50	seconds in $\frac{1}{2}$ hour	30	18 000	1800	6000	180

Paper 9

A class made this Venn diagram to show what sports they liked.

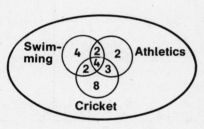

1 How many children only like cricket? ....

2 How many only like swimming? ....

3 How many just like athletics? ....

4 How many children altogether like cricket? ....

5 How many altogether like swimming? ....

6 How many altogether like athletics? ....

7 How many like both swimming and athletics? ....

8 How many like athletics and cricket? ....

9 How many like cricket and swimming? ....

10 How many like all three sports? ....

11 How many children do not like cricket? ....

12 How many do not like athletics? ....

13 How many do not like swimming? ....

14 How many children are in the class? ....

15 $3\frac{3}{4} + 2\frac{7}{8}$ 16 $7\frac{2}{3} + 4\frac{5}{9}$ 17 $1\frac{3}{5} + 2\frac{3}{10}$ 18 $8\frac{2}{7} + 3\frac{11}{14}$

....

19 $7\overline{)16 \cdot 52}$ 20 $9\overline{)0 \cdot 639}$ 21 $4\overline{)111 \cdot 00}$ 22 $11\overline{)10 \cdot 34}$

A motorist travels for 3 hours at an average speed of 60 km/h and then 2 hours at an average speed of 50 km/h.

23 How far does he go? ....

24 What is his average speed for the whole journey? ....

25 If he had travelled all the way at an average speed of 60 km/h, how long would it have taken?

....

Write the numbers in the sentences in figures.

26 It was estimated that **eight and a half million** people watched the television programme. ....

27 The population of the town is **two and a quarter million**. ....

28 The footballer was transferred to Arsenal for **£1·2 million**. ....

29 The building company made a profit of **£6·75 million**. ....

Complete the figures below. The dotted line is the line of symmetry.

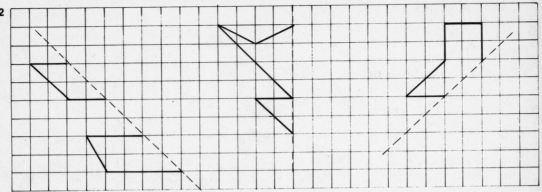

33   In a set of five tests Fiona got the following marks: 19 16 13 17 15. What was her average mark? ....

34   After one more test her average mark was 15. How many marks did she score in the sixth test? ....

35   The area of the whole shape is ....

36   The area of A is   ....

37   The area of B is   ....

38   The area of C is   ....

39   The area of D is   ....

40   The area of E is   ....

41   The perimeter of the whole shape is   ....

42   The perimeter of A is   ....

43   The perimeter of B is   ....

44   The perimeter of C is   ....

45   The perimeter of D is   ....

46   The perimeter of E is   ....

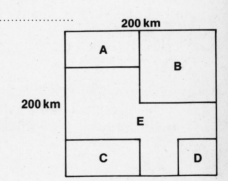

Write the following correct to one decimal place:

47 11·76 **48** 10·91 **49** 7·35 **50** 6·23

....

Paper 10

1–7 Complete this magic square containing the numbers 2 to 10. Remember that all the rows, columns and diagonals must add up to the same number (which is $\frac{1}{3}$ of the total number). It will help you to know that the number in the middle square is $\frac{1}{9}$ of the sum of all the numbers.

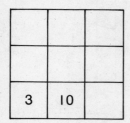

8–19 Diaries cost £2·95. Notebooks cost 65p. Rulers cost 25p. Rubbers cost 48p. Felt-tips cost 15p. Pencils cost 24p.

Complete this bill for:	£	Complete this bill for:	£
1 diary	....	5 pencils	....
2 notebooks	....	3 rulers	....
3 rubbers	....	2 diaries	....
5 felt-tips	....	6 felt-tips	....
Total	....	Total	....
Change from £10	....	Change from £10	....

At a concert 165 cups of tea were served. The number of people who asked for sugar was in the ratio of 3 : 2 to those who did not want it sweetened.

20 How many people had sugar? ....

21 How many people did not have sugar? ....

22–27 The shapes below are made of cubes. Write the number of cubes in each shape.

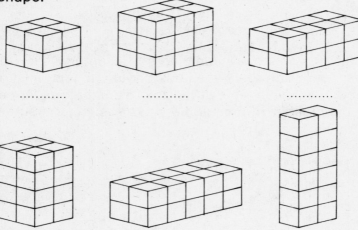

....

....

28 $\frac{7}{8}$ of 40   **29** $\frac{5}{9}$ of 27   **30** $\frac{3}{7}$ of 28   **31** $\frac{2}{11}$ of 66

....

Find the value of a in the following.

32 $6a = 36$ **33** $a - 3 = 5$ **34** $a + 4 = 7$ **35** $a + 2 = 11$

$a =$ .... $a =$ .... $a =$ .... $a =$ ....

36 $11a = 132$ **37** $\frac{a}{3} = 4$ **38** $2a = 3$ **39** $\frac{a}{5} = 4$

$a =$ .... $a =$ .... $a =$ .... $a =$ ....

Here are some annual salaries. How much are they worth per month?

40 £8100   **41** £9060   **42** £11 700   **43** £10 380

....

A worker is paid £7·50 per hour. How many hours were spent to earn each of these amounts.

44 £150

45 £262·50

46 £67·50

47 £75

....

....

....

....

Change the following to hours and minutes:

48 204 minutes

49 89 minutes

....

....

50 241 minutes

....

Paper 11

SKI PACKS		
Ski Boots		
	Adult	Child
6 DAYS	**113 FF**	**67 FF**
13 DAYS	**245 FF**	**122 FF**
Ski School $2\frac{1}{2}$ hours daily		
	Adult	Child
6 DAYS	**420 FF**	**325 FF**
12 DAYS	**840 FF**	**650 FF**
Lift Passes		
	Adult	Child
6 DAYS	**685 FF**	**480 FF**
13 DAYS	**1280 FF**	**900 FF**
Skis & Sticks		
	Adult	Child
6 DAYS	**220 FF**	**120 FF**
13 DAYS	**490 FF**	**260 FF**

Mr and Mrs Scott took their 11 year old daughter to France for a 6-day skiing holiday. They had to hire their equipment and pay for it in French francs.

1 How much did it cost for all of them to hire ski boots?   ....

2 How much did it cost for all of them to hire sticks and skis?   ....

3 They all decided to join the ski school. How much did that cost?

....

4 They all needed lift passes. How much was this?   ....

5 The total of this was   ....

6 At the time of their holiday 10 FF were equal to £1.
How much in English money did it cost to hire boots, skis
and sticks? ....

7 In English money, the ski school cost ....

8 In English money the passes for the lift cost ....

Put brackets where necessary to make the following correct:

9 $7 \times 8 - 4 = 28$

10 $7 + 2 \times 5 + 1 = 18$

11 $6 \times 9 + 6 = 60$

12 $4 \times 4 - 3 \times 3 = 7$

13 $3 \times 2 - 4 \times 1 = 2$

14 $3 + 4 + 5 \times 2 = 17$

15 $16 \div 0.02$

16 $1.2 \div 0.4$

17 $0.008 \div 4$

....

15–19 In a car park there were 100 red cars, 80 blue cars, 90 green cars,
60 cream cars and 30 others. Show this information in the Venn
diagram.

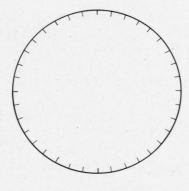

20–2

Draw lines of symmetry in the figures above. Be careful, some figures may
have more than one line and others may not have any.

30–35 In the chart below fill in the change given from a £10 note in the smallest possible number of coins.

Money spent	Change given							
	£5	£1	50p	20p	10p	5p	2p	1p
£7·76								
£5·57								
£1·38								
£2·23								
£6·14								
£2·21								

36–41 A class thought it would take exactly two minutes to run to the end of the field. Mr Jones timed them. Rashid took 118 seconds, Marilyn did it in $2\frac{1}{4}$ minutes, Karl took 107 seconds, Jasmin took 1 minute 59 seconds, Esther ran it in 2 minutes 12 seconds and Boris took 2 minutes 3 seconds. Who was the nearest to two minutes? Put them in order.

The nearest was   ....

Then   ....

Then   ....

Then   ....

Then   ....

Furthest away was   ....

42–45 Underline the numbers which are exactly divisible by 10:

1365   1270   1111   1765   2100

8080   1235   1801   3000   1681

Change the following to grams:

46 5 kg

....

47 0·3 kg

....

48 2·064 kg

....

49 11·2 kg

....

50 200 kg

....

COSTA DE ALMERIA	OCT	NOV	DEC	JAN	FEB	MAR	APR
Average daily max hours of sun	7	6	6	6	6	7	8
Average daily max temp °F	75	68	63	59	61	65	67
London °F	57	50	45	43	44	50	55

1 In Costa de Almeria, which month has the most average hours of sunshine? ....

2 Which month has the highest average temperature in Costa de Almeria? ....

3 Which month has the highest average temperature in London? ....

4 What is the difference in average temperature between London and Costa de Almeria in December? ....

5 How much difference is there between the highest and lowest temperatures shown in the Costa de Almeria? ....

6 How much difference is there between the highest and lowest temperatures shown in London? ....

7 In which month is there the least difference in temperature between the two places? ....

8 What is the difference in temperature in that month? ....

LETTERS AND POSTCARDS Europe

Not over	£	p
20 g		22
60 g		37
100 g		53
150 g		70
200 g		88

Not over	£	p
250 g	1	06
300 g	1	25
350 g	1	44
400 g	1	64
450 g	1	83

Not over	£	p
500 g	2	02
750 g	2	77
1000 g	3	52
1250 g	4	07
1500 g	4	62

Not over	£	p
1750 g	5	17
2000 g	5	72

What would it cost to send:

9 a letter weighing 15 g? ....

10 one weighing 160 g? ....

11 one weighing 505 g? ....

12 one weighing 1001 g? ....

13 one weighing 40 g? ....

14 one weighing 1959 g? ....

15 one weighing 200 g? ....

How many mg are there in:

16 3·089 g   17 1·75 g   18 0·003 g   19 0·025 g   20 0·08 g

....

Some children from our school went on a Mediterranean cruise. The chart shows some of the islands they visited and how long they stayed there.

	Port	Arrive	Depart
Saturday	Santorini	07.00	10.00
	Heraklion	15.30	19.30
Sunday	Rhodes	09.00	21.00
Monday	Patmos	07.00	09.30
	Ephesus	13.30	18.30
Tuesday	Cross Bosphorous	18.00	19.30
Thursday	Delos	14.00	22.00

21 How long did they stay on Santorini? ....

22 How long did they stay on Heraklion? ....

23 How long do you think it took to sail from Santorini to Heraklion? ....

24 How long did they stay on Rhodes? ....

25 How long did they stay on Patmos? ....

26 They stayed .... at Ephesus.

27 They crossed the Bosphorous in ....

28 They were in Delos for .... hours.

```
29      l    ml              30      l    ml
        3    70                      7    998
      - 1   157                    + 3    27
        _____                     _____


31      m    cm              32      m    cm
        7    85                      8     2
      + 3    19                    - 2    77
        _____                     _____
```

33–38 Below is a recipe for making scones. We wanted to make 120 scones for a school party. What ingredients would we need?

Scones (makes 12)   *To make 120 scones*

230 g self-raising flour   .... self-raising flour

$\frac{1}{2}$ teaspoon baking powder   .... baking powder

40 g butter or margarine   .... butter or margarine

60 g caster sugar   .... caster sugar

140 ml milk   .... milk

Using the same recipe, how many scones would we be making if we

needed I kg of butter? ....

Give the size of the marked angles below.

39    **40**    **41**    **42**

....

There are 660 pupils in a school; 55% of them are girls.

43 How many girls are in the school?   ....

44 How many boys are there?   ....

Here are James' marks for last term's tests. Make them into percentages.

45 Mathematics   40 out of 50   ....

46 English   22 out of 25   ....

47 French   13 out of 20   ....

48 Geography   21 out of 28   ....

49 History   28 out of 40   ....

50 Art   24 out of 48   ....

Paper 13

SELF DRIVE CAR HIRE RATES

Vehicle	Low Season 1 Jan–20 May 1 Oct–31 Oct	Mid Season 21 May–15 July 3 Sept–30 Sept	High Season 16 July–25 Sept
	Daily	Daily	Daily
A Fiesta	£5·50	£7·50	£8·00
B Escort	£6·75	£8·75	£9·50
C Sierra	£9·50	£11·50	£12·00
D Montego	£16·00	£18·00	£20·75
E Minibus	£18·75	£21·50	£22·75

How much does it cost to hire:

1 A minibus for 4 days in June? ....

2 An Escort for 5 days in August? ....

3 A Montego for 6 days in April? ....

4 A Sierra for 3 days in February? ....

5 A Fiesta for 5 days during the first week in July? ....

6 How much more does it cost to hire a Sierra than an Escort for 6 days in mid-September? ....

7 How much less does it cost to hire a Montego than a minibus for 4 days in August? ....

8 $178 + 35 - $ .... $= 197$

9 $241 - 59 + $ .... $= 231$

10 $31 \times 11 - $ .... $= 315$

11
```
   6378
   2589
+  1765
_____
```

12
```
 10001
-   929
_____
```

13
```
  4768
×    8
_____
```

14 $12\overline{)8160}$

15 £
    303·03
  − 78·87
  _____

16 £
    515·15
  − 357·91
  _____

17 £
    264·75
  ×   7
  _____

18 £
    9) 341·64

19–27 Put the following numbers in the Venn diagram:

Set A = prime numbers < 15
Set B = odd numbers < 15
Set C = multiples of 5 < 15

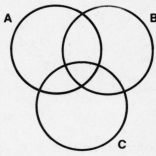

28 Add the largest number below to the smallest.

2·3   2·003   2·033   2·303   2·030   ....

29 Subtract the smallest number below from the largest.

10·007   10·077   10·708   10·070   10·780   ....

30 The average of four numbers is $5\frac{1}{2}$. If one of the numbers is 7, what is the average of the other 3 numbers? ....

How many minutes are there in:

31 $4\frac{1}{4}$ hours   32 $7\frac{1}{10}$ hours   33 $2\frac{3}{5}$ hours

....

34–36 Three numbers multiplied together equal 2880.
A × B = 360, A × C = 160

A = ...   B = ...   C = ...

37–42 Put these in order, starting with the one which is the best value.

A   20 g for £2   B   25 g for £3   C   30 g for £4·20
D   10 g for £1·30   E   24 g for £2·64   F   40 g for £3·60

....

36

43   kg
       29·74
    +92·47
    ———————

44   l
       31·13
    −17·71
    ———————

We went to Green's Nurseries where we found that all the prices had been increased by 20%.

45 Pot plant

Was £3·20

Now ....

46 Tub of fertiliser

Was £6·70

Now ....

47 Watering can

Was £5·80

Now ....

48 Flower pots

Were £1·80 for 10

Now ....

49 Gardening gloves

Were £4·45

Now ....

50 Rose bush

Was £9·50

Now ....

Paper 14

1–16 Below are the marks gained by 20 children in a test. First complete the table below, then complete the histogram:

19	20	17	20
17	17	13	15
16	18	16	17
17	13	17	16
18	15	17	17

Mark   Frequency

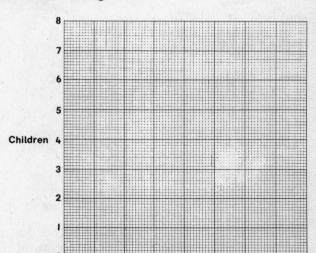

17   km
     37·26
  ×   8

18   m

$$11\overline{)85{\cdot}91}$$

19–24 Complete the following table:

Average speed in km/h	Time taken in hours	Distance covered in km
28	3	....
38	....	19
....	....	9
240	....	360
....	$2\frac{1}{2}$	250
48	5	....

Insert signs to make the following correct:

25 7   3   4 = 16

26 9   7   8 = 8

27 5   5   7 = 16   2

28 12   2   3 = 3   3

29 6   5   4 = 5   3

30 10   2   4 = 6   3

31–34 Underline the fractions below which have a value less than 2.

$\frac{9}{3}$ $\frac{35}{20}$ $\frac{17}{8}$ $\frac{13}{7}$ $\frac{50}{40}$ $\frac{11}{4}$ $\frac{19}{8}$ $\frac{14}{9}$

35 Mark was very pleased when he gained 80% in his French test. If the marks were out of 40, how many marks did Mark receive?

....

Give the area and perimeter of the following shapes:

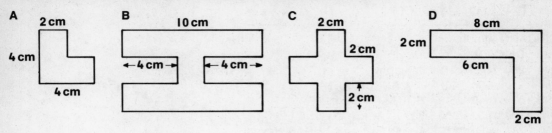

A 2 cm 4 cm 4 cm
B 10 cm ←4 cm→ ←4 cm→
C 2 cm 2 cm 2 cm
D 8 cm 2 cm 6 cm 2 cm

36 Area of A ....

37 Perimeter of A ....

38 Area of B ....

39 Perimeter of B ....

40 Area of C ....

41 Perimeter of C ....

42 Area of D ....

43 Perimeter of D ....

44 What is the length of one side of an equilateral triangle if the perimeter of the triangle is 10·5 cm? ....

45–50 Angus, Belinda and Christine had £1·68 between them. After Angus paid back the 3p that he had borrowed from Belinda, and Christine had repaid 5p she had borrowed from Belinda, they found that Angus had twice as much as Belinda, and Belinda had twice as much as Christine.

At first: Angus had .... Belinda had ....

Christine had ....

Afterwards: Angus had .... Belinda had ....

Christine had ....

Paper 15

CHICAGO Illinois										
1020	**DENVER** Colorado									
270	1280	**DETROIT** Michigan								
1650	710	1900	**GRAND CANYON** Ariz.							
1090	1030	1340	1210	**HOUSTON** Texas						
1010	1700	1000	1800	920	**JACKSONVILLE** Flor.					
1770	780	2030	310	1420	2100	**LAS VEGAS** Nevada				
2100	1130	2350	530	1550	2390	280	**LOS ANGELES** Cal.			
1410	2060	1440	2310	1230	360	2520	2730	**MIAMI** Florida		
850	1860	570	2510	1860	1400	2590	2920	1790	**MONTREAL** Quebec	
940	1280	1090	1540	360	590	1720	1900	910	1640	**NEW ORLEANS** Louis.

Distances are in miles.

Look at the chart, then answer the questions.

1   What is the distance between Chicago and Miami?   ....

2   How far is it from Detroit to Houston?   ....

3   Between Denver and Montreal it is   ....

4   The distance between Grand Canyon and New Orleans is   ....

5   How much further is it from Jacksonville to Miami than from Grand Canyon to Las Vegas?   ....

6   Which two places listed are the shortest distance apart?   ....

7   Which two places listed are the greatest distance apart?   ....

8   Which two places are exactly 1700 miles apart?   ....

9   Which two places are exactly 1000 miles apart?   ....

10   Which two places are exactly 1800 miles apart?   ....

11   Which two sets of places are exactly 1900 miles apart?   ....

12   ....

13 A typist averages 14 words to a line and 30 lines to a page. How many pages will be needed for 38 406 words? ....

Find:

14 $\frac{3}{5}$ of 25   15 $\frac{4}{7}$ of $\frac{28}{36}$ 16 $\frac{7}{8}$ of 2   17 $\frac{9}{10}$ of $\frac{50}{63}$

....

Car park charges	
Up to 1 hour	80p
1 to 2 hours	£1·00
2 to 3 hours	£1·20
3 to 4 hours	£1·40
4 to 5 hours	£1·60
5 to 6 hours	£1·80
6 to 7 hours	£2·00
7 to 8 hours	£2·10
Over 8 and up to 12 hours	£3·00

What would the following people pay:

18 Mr Dee parked from 11.30am to 1.15pm.   ....

19 Mrs Gee parked from 10.20am to 1.25pm.   ....

20 Mr Exe parked from 9.25am to 2.10pm.   ....

21 Mrs Ward parked from 8.30am to 5.05pm.   ....

22 Mr Kent parked from 1.05pm to 2.10pm.   ....

23 Mrs Bell parked from 2.17pm to 10.01pm.   ....

24 Mr Green parked from 10.44am to 4.05pm.   ....

Change to centimetres.

25 47·5 m   26 0·176 m   27 6·07 m   28 103·03 m

....

Change to grams.

29 0·37 kg   30 11 kg   31 0·002 kg   32 4·15 kg

....

33-44 Complete the table below:

Fraction	Decimal	Percentage
$\frac{9}{10}$	....	....
....	0·01	....
....	....	17%
....	0·3	....
$\frac{11}{20}$	....	....
$\frac{17}{25}$	....	....

Round off these numbers to the nearest whole number:

45 4·55   46 17·19   47 1·03

....

48 2·49   49 7·09   50 46·7

....

Paper 16

What is the remainder when:

1 7 is divided into 30   2 8 is divided into 60

....

3 9 is divided into 100   4 11 is divided into 120

....

5 12 is divided into 90   6 6 is divided into 59

....

Here is part of a train timetable:

Train	Greasby	Upton	Moreton	Leasowe
A	13.15	13.23	13.29	13.50
B	14.09	→	→	14.38
C	14.23	14.32	14.39	14.59
D	15.01	→	→	15.31
E	15.58	16.07	16.14	16.32

7 Travelling from Greasby to Leasowe, which train is the fastest? ....

8 Which is the slowest? ....

9 Which two trains are non-stop? ....

10 If I cannot leave Greasby before 3.30pm, which of these trains must I catch? ....

11 How long does train E take to go from Greasby to Upton? ....

12 How long does train A take to travel from Upton to Leasowe? ....

13–15 Share £45·00 in the ratio 2 : 3 : 4. ....

16–18 Share £34·00 among A, B and C so that A has £2 more than B and C has £1 less than B.

A B C
....

19–21 Share £18·00 among A, B and C so that A has three times as much as B, and B has twice as much as C.

A B C
....

Give the value of 1 in the following numbers:

22 28·01   23 17·65   24 321·6   25 9·1   26 145·6

....

27–42 Some children from our school went on a day trip to London. The cost was £20·00 per child.

Class	Number in class	Number going on trip
2a	30	6
2b	30	7
3a	30	8
3b	30	4
4a	30	13
4b	30	12

Make a spike graph to show how much money was collected from each class. Two numbers have been inserted to help you arrange the money in the best way.

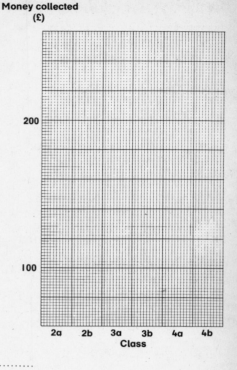

Money collected (£)

What fraction of all the children from these classes went on this trip? ....

Louise spends $\frac{1}{4}$ of her money on fruit and $\frac{5}{8}$ on a magazine. She has 20p left.

43 How much did she have at first? ....

44 How much did she spend on fruit? ....

45 How much did the magazine cost? ....

46 What fraction of her money did she have left? ....

The perimeter of a piece of card is 100 cm and it is four times as long as it is wide.

47 The length is ....   **48** The width is ....

What is the length of the side of the square whose area is:

49 196 cm²   **50** 289 cm²

....

Paper 17

1–13 Enter the information below on the Venn diagram.

Four children like both table tennis and darts.
One child likes both table tennis and chess.
Two like both darts and chess.
Five children like all three games.
Three children do not like any of the games.

Next, enter this information:

31 children altogether like table tennis.
23 children altogether like darts.
15 children altogether like chess.

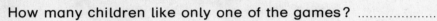

Now answer the following questions:

How many children like only one of the games? ....

How many children like two of the games? ....

How many do not like table tennis? ....

How many do not like darts? ....

How many do not like chess? ....

14–23 At an end-of-season sale, prices were slashed by 25%.

Items bought	Usual price	Sale price	Saving
Table cloth	£9·60	....	....
Pullover	£22·00	....	....
Dress	....	£33·75	....
Child's suit	....	£12·00	....
Slippers	....	£3·60	....

24–30 Underline the correct answer:

$\frac{1}{3} \div 3$	= 1	$\frac{4}{3}$	$\frac{1}{9}$	$\frac{1}{2}$	9
days in 1990	= 300	366	160	350	365
$\frac{1}{3} + \frac{4}{9}$	= $\frac{7}{9}$	$\frac{5}{12}$	$\frac{5}{9}$	$\frac{4}{9}$	$\frac{2}{3}$

45

1% of 1000	= 100	10	1	1000	101
3030 g	= 303 kg	30·3 kg	3·03 kg	3·003 kg	0·303 kg
515 cm	= 5·15 m	0·515 m	51·5 m	5150 m	515·5 m
40% of 25	= 65	15	12·5	8	10

31 Area of whole shape   ....

32 Area of shaded part   ....

33 Area of unshaded part   ....

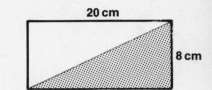

34–45 Give the co-ordinates of the letters:

A   ....   B   ....

C   ....   D   ....

E   ....   F   ....

G   ....   H   ....

J   ....   K   ....

L   ....   M   ....

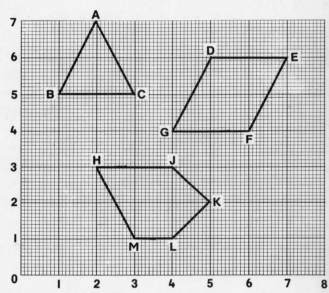

46–50 Put these fractions in order of size, smallest first:

$\frac{9}{10}$	$\frac{1}{2}$	$\frac{3}{4}$	$\frac{11}{20}$	$\frac{4}{5}$
....	....	....	....	....

Paper 18

Indicate which is the larger by writing > or < in each space.

1 24 × 4   25 + 60   2 9 + 8 − 4   20 − 2 − 6

3 5 × 11   7 × 8   4 9 × 12   10 × 11

5 7 × 10   6 × 12   6 3 + 7 + 9   2 + 9 + 6

In each of the figures below, give the area of the whole shape, the area of the shaded part and the area of the unshaded section.

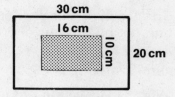

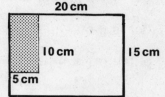

7   Area of whole   ....

8   Area of shaded part   ....

9   Area of unshaded part ....

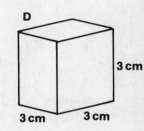

10 Area of whole   ....

11 Area of shaded part   ....

12 Area of unshaded part ....

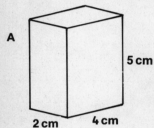

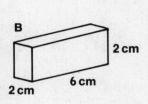

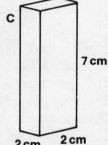

A

5 cm

2 cm   4 cm

B

2 cm

2 cm   6 cm

C

7 cm

2 cm   2 cm

D

3 cm

3 cm   3 cm

13 The volume of figure A is   ....

14 The volume of figure B is   ....

15 The capacity of figure C is ....

16 The capacity of figure D is ....

If the sides of each figure were twice as large, the volume of each would be:

17 Figure A   ....   18 Figure B   ....

19 Figure C   ....   20 Figure D   ....

How many:

21 $\frac{1}{4}$s are there in $4\frac{1}{2}$?   ....   22 $\frac{1}{5}$s in $7\frac{3}{5}$?   ....

23 $\frac{1}{3}$s in $7\frac{2}{3}$?   ....   24 $\frac{1}{12}$s in $6\frac{1}{3}$?   ....

25 $\frac{1}{10}$s in $5\frac{1}{2}$?   ....   26 $\frac{1}{7}$s in $5\frac{5}{7}$?   ....

47

27 Felt-tip pens cost a shopkeeper £1·80 for 10. How many can he buy for £36·00? ....

28 Carelessly, Lena divided by 8 instead of multiplying by 8 and got an answer of 564. What should it have been? ....

$\frac{5}{9}$ of a sum of money is 45p.

29 What is the whole amount? ....

30 What is $\frac{2}{9}$ of it? ....

31 $\frac{2}{3}$ of the amount is ....

32 What is my average speed if I travel 20 km in 15 minutes? ....

33 At the same speed, how far would I go in $\frac{3}{4}$ hour? ....

34–42 Potatoes are 16p per kg. Cauliflowers are 35p each. Onions are 36p per kg. Parsley is 15p a bunch. Cabbage is 27p per kg. Sprouts are 48p per kg.

Complete the following bills:

	£		£
2 kg cabbage	....	2½ kg sprouts	....
2 cauliflowers	....	6 kg potatoes	....
3 kg onions	....	2 bunches parsley	....
Total	....	3 cauliflowers	....
		Total	....

We are at school from 8.45am to noon and 1.30 to 4.00pm.

43 How long are we at school in the morning? ....

44 How long are we at school in the afternoon? ....

45 In one day we are at school for ....

46 In a school week (five days) we are at school for

....

47 What number when multiplied by 36 gives the same answer as 42 × 18?

....

48 How many books, each costing 95p, can be bought for £42·75?

....

49 A man's salary was £12750. He was given an increase of 10%. How much does he earn now?

....

50 What is the smallest number that 8, 5, 4 and 10 will all divide into without a remainder?

....

Paper 19

Multiply each of the numbers below by 100.

1	0·0017	2	3·009	3	2·75	4	468·6	5	17

....

Write in figures the following numbers:

6 Four hundred and nine thousand and seventeen

....

7 Two hundred thousand and ten

....

8 Half a million

....

9 Nineteen thousand, one hundred and ninety one

....

10 Twenty-seven thousand and four

....

11 One hundred thousand, one hundred and one

....

12-25 Here are the shoe sizes of 20 children. First complete the table below and then complete the histogram.

2 3 2 1
$1\frac{1}{2}$ $2\frac{1}{2}$ $1\frac{1}{2}$ $1\frac{1}{2}$
$2\frac{1}{2}$ $3\frac{1}{2}$ 3 4
$2\frac{1}{2}$ 4 3 $3\frac{1}{2}$
3 $2\frac{1}{2}$ 4 $2\frac{1}{2}$

Shoe size   Frequency

....

....

....

....

....

....

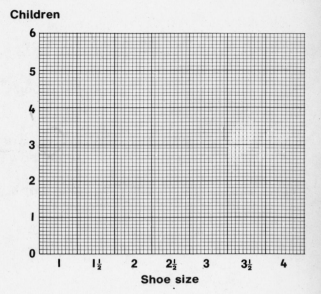

If you turn in a clockwise direction, which way would you be facing if:

26 you are facing south and turn through 135° ....

27 you are facing NW and turn through 90° ....

28 you are facing SE and turn through 45° ....

29 you are facing SW and turn through 270° ....

30 you are facing NE and turn through 180° ....

31 you are facing N and turn through 315° ....

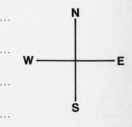

A bottle of concentrated orange drink holds 1·25 litres. The glasses each hold 300 ml. We need to put 50 ml of orange in each glass before adding water.

32 What fraction of the glass did the orange concentrate fill? ....

33 How many glasses could we make from a bottle of orange drink? ....

34 175 people asked for a drink. How many bottles of the orange would be needed? ....

35 If each bottle costs 75p, how much would this be? ....

36 If we charged 10p a glass and sold all we had, what profit would we make? ....

37 Andrew's bus fare to school is 37p. If he travels to and from school each day, how much does this cost per day? ....

38 How much does it cost for a school week (5 days)? ....

39 How many trips could he make for £5·00? ....

40 How much change would be over? ....

41–43 Complete the figures below. The dotted line is the line of symmetry.

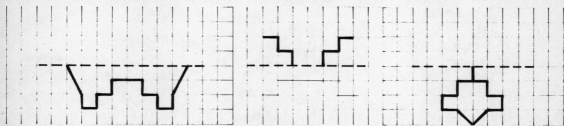

44–50 In the chart below, fill in the change from a £20 note which uses the smallest number of coins possible.

Amount spent	Change given								
	£10	£5	£1	50p	20p	10p	5p	2p	1p
£11·17									
£9·09									
£8·13									
£14·41									
£18·08									
£7·23									
£10·05									

Paper 20

What is the square root of:

1 100   2 64   3 36   4 25   5 1

....

Find the value of a if:

6 $a + 3 - 2 = 5$ 7 $a - 3 - 2 = 1$ 8 $3a = 13 - 1$

....

9 $2a + 5 = 15$ 10 $4a + 2 = 18$ 11 $3a - 2 + 3 = 7$

....

12 $\frac{2}{5}$ of a number is 10. What is the number?   ....

13–20 Here is a recipe for Eccles cakes. It makes 20 cakes. In the spaces provided, write the quantities required to make enough for 100 people.

Eccles cakes (for 20)	Eccles cakes (for 100)
225 g plain flour	.... plain flour
175 g margarine	.... margarine
Salt	Salt
Water to mix	Water to mix
Filling	Filling
75 g butter	.... butter
200 g brown sugar	.... brown sugar
150 g currants	.... currants
1 tsp cinnamon	.... cinnamon
$\frac{1}{2}$ tsp nutmeg	.... tsp nutmeg
50 g chopped peel	.... chopped peel

52

What time is:

21 35 minutes after 2.40pm

....

22 49 minutes before 3.10pm

....

23 46 minutes after 11.25pm

....

24 49 minutes before noon

....

25–30 Underline the correct answer:

Degrees in half a right angle	50	60	90	45	120
Minutes in $2\frac{1}{2}$ hours	120	150	140	160	200
2^3	8	6	2	4	12
Hours in November	600	300	700	800	720
Millimetres in 2 metres	1000	100	2000	200	20
cm³ in 1 litre	100	10	50	1000	2000

What fraction is shaded in the following circles?

31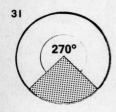

32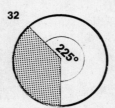

33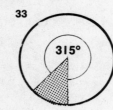

34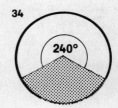

....

35–38 What is the total surface area of the following shapes?

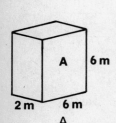

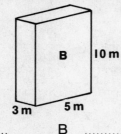

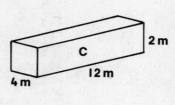

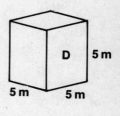

A ....   B ....   C ....   D ....

Round off the numbers below to the nearest 100.

39 17 864   40 28 043   41 92 092   42 50 705

....

43–50 What percentage of each shape is shaded?
Write the answer in the space provided.

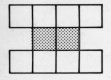 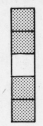 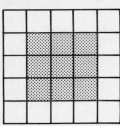

....

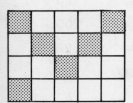 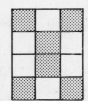 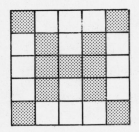 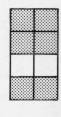

....

Paper 21

How much does it cost to
post a parcel weighing:

1   $5\frac{1}{2}$ kg   ....

2   $8\frac{1}{4}$ kg   ....

3   900 g   ....

4   $6\frac{3}{4}$ kg   ....

5   3·3 kg   ....

6   770 g   ....

PARCEL POST

Weight not over	£	p	Weight not over	£	p
1 kg	1	60	7 kg	3	25
2 kg	2	00	8 kg	3	40
3 kg	2	45	9 kg	3	60
4 kg	2	65	10 kg	3	75
5 kg	2	90	25 kg	4	75
6 kg	3	10			

A man leaves A at 9.00am, travelling at an average speed of 60 km/h. His friend
leaves B at the same time, his average speed being 40 km/h. They travel
towards each other and meet at C at 11.30am.

7   How far apart are A and B?   ....

54

8 How far is *C* from *A*? ....

9 How far is *B* from *C*? ....

10 How long would it take the first man to cover the whole distance from *A* to *B*? ....

11 How long would the other man take? ....

Change the following fractions to percentages:

12 $\frac{1}{5}$ **13** $\frac{1}{40}$ **14** $\frac{1}{20}$

....

15 $\frac{1}{50}$ **16** $\frac{2}{5}$ **17** $\frac{3}{5}$

....

18
km	m	cm
2	40	90
+5	990	75

19
m	cm	mm
7	2	7
−4	2	8

20
m	cm	mm

8) 8   9   6

21-23 The ages of our family add up to 85 years. I am 10 years old, Dad is $3\frac{1}{2}$ times as old as I am. My sister is 2 years younger than I am and Mum is 4 times as old as my sister.

Mum is .... Dad is .... My sister is ....

24-35

Station	Train A	Train B	Train C	
Ashton	7.58	....	....	Fill in the times of Trains B and C which take the
Burford	8.05	....	....	same time as A to travel between the stations.
Colby	8.17	....	....	B starts 25 minutes later than A and C starts 45
Downton	8.31	....	....	minutes later than A.
Everby	8.40	....	....	
Frankby	8.59	....	....	

55

Give the co-ordinates of the towns listed below. Some may not be situated on the lines but are inside the squares. When this is so, the co-ordinates of the bottom left-hand corner of the square should be used.

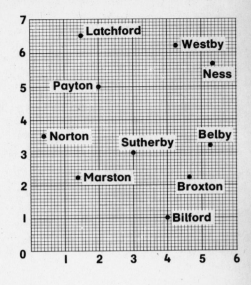

Ness ....   Marston ....

Bilford ....   Norton ....

Name the towns which have the following co-ordinates:

4, 2 ....   4, 6 ....

5, 3 ....   1, 6 ....

2, 5 ....   3, 3 ....

46–48 Grandad gave us £20. Mum said it would be fairest to share it among us in the ratio of our ages. I am 11, my brother is 9 and my sister is 5.

I got ....   My brother received ....   My sister had ....

There are 1020 children in a school. 55% of the pupils are girls.

49 How many girls are there? ....

50 How many boys are there? ....

Paper 22

Give the answers to the following in the lowest terms:

1 $\frac{7}{8} \times \frac{40}{49}$ 2 $\frac{4}{9} \times \frac{27}{24}$ 3 $\frac{5}{11} \times \frac{66}{50}$ 4 $\frac{4}{5} \times \frac{20}{28}$

....

5 Three numbers multiplied together give 2618. One number is 11 and another is 14. What is the third number? ....

56

6–13 Here are some of Tamsin's test marks. Fill in her percentage marks.

	Mark	Out of	Percentage
English	$8\frac{1}{2}$	10	....
Maths	13	20	....
French	19	25	....
History	21	28	....

In the same tests, here are Simon's percentage marks. Fill in his actual marks.

		Out of	Percentage
English	....	10	60
Maths	....	20	75
French	....	25	84
History	....	28	50

On one bank holiday 6300 people went to the zoo. The ratio of children to adults was 4 : 1.

14 How many children went to the zoo? ....

15 How many adults went? ....

The ratio of boys to girls was 6 : 4.

16 How many boys went? ....

17 How many girls? ....

The ratio of men to women was 3 : 4.

18 How many men went to the zoo? ....

19 How many women? ....

20
```
    £
  468·29
  359·46
+ 217·38
_____

_____
```

21
```
    £
  1000·10
-  789·98
_____

_____
```

22
```
    £
  184·65
×      7
_____

_____
```

23
```
    £
6)2125·50
```

We helped our teacher work out the cost of our class going to a show. The charges were as follows:

The first 10 children   £2·00 each   Over 20 and up to 25   £1·60 each
Over 10 and up to 15   £1·80 each   Over 25 and up to 30   £1·50 each
Over 15 and up to 20   £1·70 each

24   There are 24 children in our class. How much would it cost to take all of us? ....

25   How much is this shared out equally? Answer to the nearest penny ....

26   Unfortunately, three children got measles and so only 21 were able to go. What is the total cost of taking us now? ....

27   How much is this shared equally? Answer to the nearest penny. ....

28   How many children could be taken if £50 was spent on the tickets? ....

29–34   Complete the following chart:

Wholesale price (Price at factory) (£)	Retail price (Price in shop) (£)	Profit (£)
£8·85	£15·50	....
£38·38	....	£16·87
....	£35·25	£10·49
£97·78	£135·75	....
£95·99	....	£45·51
....	£26·25	£8·48

35–50   Insert a sign in each space to make each line and column work out to the given answer.

2		3		4	=	10
4		1		2	=	3
2		4		3	=	5
=		=		=		=
8		1		5	=	2

Paper 23

1–8 Put this information in the diagram.

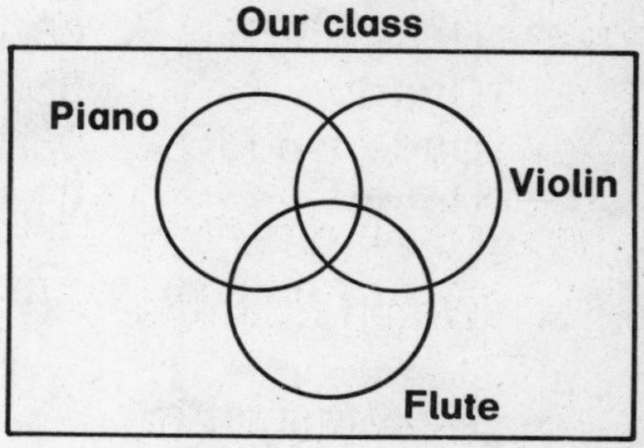

5 children play both the violin and the piano
6 play both the piano and the flute
1 plays the violin and the flute
2 play all three instruments
2 do not play any of the instruments

Complete the diagram by entering this information:

27 children altogether play the piano, 14 altogether play the violin, and 18 altogether play the flute.

9 How many children play one instrument only? ....

10 How many play two instruments? ....

11 How many children do not play the piano? ....

12 How many do not play the violin? ....

13 How many do not play the flute? ....

14–19 Write the number which has:

a 7 in the tenths place
a 5 in the tens place
a 2 in the units place
a 6 in the thousandths place
a 1 in the hundreds place
an 8 in the hundredths place. ....

20–22 We collected £21·00, which was made up of 20p, 10p and 5p coins. We found that there were twice as many 20p coins as 10p coins, and twice as many 10p as 5p.

There were:

.... 20p coins .... 10p coins .... 5p coins

23 What number multiplied by 45 will give the same answer as

65 × 27? ....

Station	Train A	Train B	Train C	Train D
Caldy	08.13	09.42	18.01	19.47
Ness	08.24	09.51	17.47	19.36
Overton	08.37	10.07	17.33	19.19
Underwood	08.50	10.20	17.18	19.05
Upton	09.11	10.43	16.59	18.47

24 Which is the fastest of these trains?   ....

25 Next fastest is   ....

26 The third fastest is   ....

27 The slowest is   ....

28 How long does the fastest train take to travel from
Ness to Upton?   ....

29 How long does Train C take to travel from Underwood
to Ness?   ....

30 If I live in Ness and want to be in Upton by 9.30am,
which train must I catch?   ....

31 At what time should the 19.05 train from Underwood
arrive in Ness?   ....

32 If I travel from Overton to Upton on the 10.07
train and return on the 18.47, how long do
I have in Upton?   ....

Here are the ages of six friends

	years	months
Simon	11	6
Zoe	10	11
Pippa	11	1
Andrew	10	10
Carl	11	11
Barry	11	3

33 Their ages add up to: ....

34 Their average age is: ....

35 Another girl joins them and their average age is now 11 years 2 months. How old is the newcomer?

....

36–50 Complete the following chart. All shapes are regular and measurements are in cm.

Length	Width	Perimeter	Area	Shape
10	....	....	....	square
8	7	....	....	....
....	6	30	....	....
....	....	....	64	square
11	....	....	....	square

Paper 24

1 How many minutes are there in 48 hours? ....

2 How many days are there in 264 hours? ....

3 How many seconds are there in 790 minutes? ....

A newsagent sold 720 magazines to adults and children. This pie chart gives you details.

4 Women bought .... magazines

5 Men bought .... magazines

6 Girls bought .... magazines

7 Boys bought .... magazines

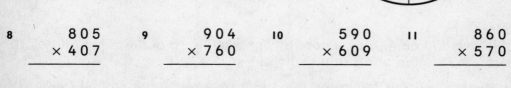

8	9	10	11
805 × 407	904 × 760	590 × 609	860 × 570

Three sums of money total £100. The largest amount is £46·80, the second largest is three times as large as the smallest.

12 The second largest amount is ....

13 The smallest amount is ....

14 $1\frac{1}{2} \div 1\frac{3}{4}$ 15 $1\frac{3}{4} \div 3\frac{1}{2}$ 16 $2\frac{1}{4} \div 1\frac{1}{2}$ 17 $3\frac{2}{3} \div 1\frac{5}{6}$

....

18–31 Here is a graph which shows the results of a test.
Using the following information, complete the chart below to show the marks of the boys and girls separately.

The ratio of girls to boys in the 90–100 group was 2 : 1.

50% of the 80–89 group were boys, and 3 times as many boys as girls gained 70–79.

$\frac{4}{10}$ of those in the 60–69 group were boys, and $\frac{2}{3}$ of those gaining 50–59 were girls.

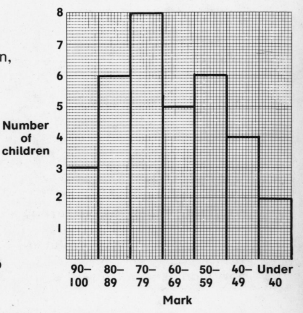

$\frac{3}{4}$ of the 40–49 group were boys and one boy gained less than 40 marks.

	Boys	Girls		Boys	Girls
90–100	....	....	50–59	....	....
80–89	....	....	40–49	....	....
70–79	....	....	Under 40	....	....
60–69	....	....			

264 children go home from school by bus. One-third of them get off before we reach the station and $\frac{5}{8}$ of these children are girls.

32 How many girls leave the bus before we reach the station? ....

33 How many boys leave the bus before we reach the station? ....

34–36 In a village the population is 1010. The men and women together number 451 and the women and children together number 795.

There are .... men .... women .... children

A bus holds 88 passengers. On the first part of the journey it was three-quarters full, and on the second part there were seven times as many seats occupied as were empty.

37 How many people travelled on the first part of the journey? ....

38 How many people on the second part? ....

39 What number is half way between 29 and 71? ....

Julian went out on his bicycle one morning.

40 How far had Julian gone by 10am?

....

41 For how long did he stop?

....

42 What was his average cycling speed?

....

43 How far from home was he at 11am?

....

44 How far did he travel between 11.15 and 11.30am?

....

45 Gina also started out at 9am and finished at 11.30. She travelled at 30 km/h. Draw in a line to show Gina's journey.

46 How far apart are Julian and Gina at 10am? ....

47 How far apart are they at 10.30am? ....

48 I have £9·00. How many articles, each costing 59p, can I buy? ....

49 How much change will I receive? ....

50 How much more money would I need to buy another three
  articles? ....

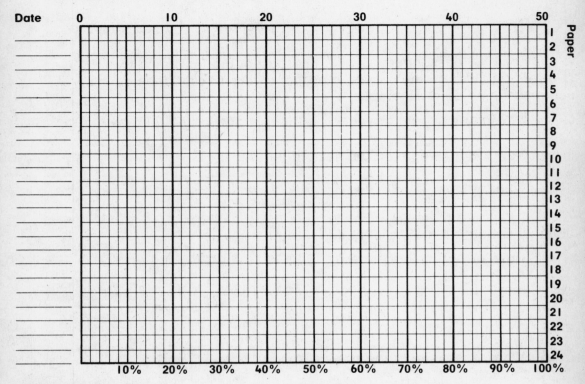

Thomas Nelson and Sons Ltd
Nelson House   Mayfield Road
Walton-on-Thames   Surrey
KT12 5PL   UK

51 York Place
Edinburgh EH1 3JD   UK

Thomas Nelson (Hong Kong) Ltd
Toppan Building 10/F   22A Westlands Road
Quarry Bay   Hong Kong

Distributed in Australia by

Thomas Nelson Australia
480 La Trobe Street
Melbourne   Victoria 3000
and in Sydney, Brisbane, Adelaide and Perth

© **J M Bond 1988**
First published by Thomas Nelson and Sons Ltd 1988

Pupil's Book ISBN 0-17-424489-4
NCN 987654321
Answer Book ISBN 0-17-424490-8

Filmset in Nelson Teaching Alphabet
by Mould Type Foundry Ltd
Dunkirk Lane   Leyland   Preston   England

Printed in England
by Ebenzer Baylis & Son Ltd
The Trinity Press   Worcester and London